FROM LITTLE TO BIG

A Parade of Animal Poems

FROM LITTLE

Illustrated by *June Goldsborough*

TO BIG

A Parade of Animal Poems

Compiled by *Eleanor Graham Vance*

FOLLETT PUBLISHING COMPANY
Chicago

ACKNOWLEDGMENTS

The compiler and publisher wish to express their appreciation to the publishers and persons listed below for permission to reproduce the following poems:

"Firefly" by Elizabeth Madox Roberts. From *Under the Tree* by Elizabeth Madox Roberts. Copyright 1922 by B. W. Huebsch, Inc., renewed 1950 by Ivor S. Roberts. Reprinted by permission of The Viking Press, Inc.

"The Tickle Rhyme" by Ian Serraillier. Reprinted by permission of the author.

"The Goldfish" by Dorothy Aldis. Reprinted by permission of G. P. Putnam's Sons from *All Together* by Dorothy Aldis. Copyright © 1925, 1926, 1952 by Dorothy Aldis.

"The House of the Mouse" by Lucy Sprague Mitchell. From the book *Another Here and Now Story Book* by Lucy Sprague Mitchell. Copyright 1937 by E. P. Dutton & Co., Inc. Renewal, ©, 1965 by Lucy Sprague Mitchell. Reprinted with permission of the publisher.

"For a Bird" by Myra Cohn Livingston. From *The Moon and A Star*, © 1965 by Myra Cohn Livingston. Reprinted by permission of Harcourt Brace Jovanovich, Inc.

"Sally and Manda" by Alice B. Campbell. From *Child Life Magazine*, Copyright 1934, 1962 by Rand McNally & Company.

"Baby Chick" by Aileen Fisher. Reprinted from *Runny Days, Sunny Days* by Aileen Fisher. By permission of Abelard-Schuman, Ltd. All rights reserved. Copyright year 1958.

"The Little Turtle" by Vachel Lindsay. Reprinted with permission of The Macmillan Company from *Collected Poems of Vachel Lindsay* by Vachel Lindsay. Copyright 1920 by The Macmillan Company, renewed 1948 by Elizabeth C. Lindsay.

"Fishing" by Ivy O. Eastwick. Reprinted by permission of David McKay Company, Inc. from *Rainbow Over All* by Ivy O. Eastwick. Copyright © 1967 by Ivy O. Eastwick and Anne Siberell.

"Sizes" by Eleanor Graham Vance. Printed by permission of the author.

"Mr. Rabbit" by Dixie Willson. Reprinted by permission of the author.

"Our Pussy Cat" by Alice White North. Printed by permission of the author.

"Pet" by Eleanor Graham Vance. Printed by permission of the author.

"I Like Dogs" by Margaret Wise Brown. Used by permission. From *The Golden Friendly Book* by Margaret Wise Brown. Copyright 1954 Western Publishing Company, Inc.

"Mr. Goat Explains" by Al Graham. From *Songs for a Small Guitar*, © 1962 by Al Graham and Tony Palazzo. Reprinted by permission of the author and Mrs. Philomena Palazzo.

"Foal" by Mary Britton Miller. Reprinted by permission of the author.

"The Neck" by Ilo Orleans. From *Zoo That Grew* by Ilo Orleans. Henry Z. Walck, Inc. By permission of Friede Orleans Joffee.

"Why Nobody Pets the Lion at the Zoo" by John Ciardi. Reprinted in part from the book *The Reason for the Pelican* by John Ciardi. Copyright, ©, 1959 by John Ciardi. Reprinted by permission of J. B. Lippincott Company.

"Furry Bear" by A. A. Milne. From the book *Now We Are Six* by A. A. Milne. Copyright 1927 by E. P. Dutton & Co., Inc. Renewal, ©, 1955 by A. A. Milne. Reprinted with permission of the publisher.

"Bigger" by Dorothy Brown Thompson. Reprinted by permission of the author. First published in *Child Life Magazine*.

"Camel" by Maxine Kumin. From *No One Writes a Letter to the Snail* by Maxine Kumin. Copyright © 1962 by Maxine Kumin. Reprinted by permission of G. P. Putnam's Sons.

"Rhinoceros" by Julia Hurd Strong. Reprinted by permission of the author.

"Holding Hands" by Lenore M. Link. Reprinted from *St. Nicholas* by permission of Herbert R. Mayes.

Every effort has been made to trace the owners of copyright material in this book. Should any material have been included inadvertently without the permission of the copyright owner, acknowledgment will be made in any future edition.

ISBN 0 695-40235-8 Titan binding
ISBN 0 695-80235-6 Trade binding
Library of Congress Catalog Card Number: 74-159324

CL

OCT 9 '82

First Printing

Firefly

A little light is going by,
Is going up to see the sky,
A little light with wings.

I never could have thought of it,
To have a little bug all lit
And made to go on wings.

Elizabeth Madox Roberts

5

The Tickle Rhyme

"Who's that tickling my back?" said the wall.
"Me," said a small
Caterpillar. "I'm learning
To crawl."

Ian Serraillier

The Goldfish

My darling little goldfish
Hasn't any toes;
He swims around without a sound
And bumps his hungry nose.

He can't get out to play with me,
Nor I get in to him,
Although I say: "Come out and play,"
And he—"Come in and swim."

Dorothy Aldis

The House of the Mouse

The house of the mouse
is a wee little house,
a green little house in the grass,
which big clumsy folk
may hunt and may poke
and still never see as they pass
this sweet little, neat little,
wee little, green little,
cuddle-down hide-away
house in the grass.

Lucy Sprague Mitchell

For a Bird

I found him lying near the tree; I folded up his wings.
   Oh, little bird,
   You never heard
   The song the summer sings.

I wrapped him in a shirt I wore in winter; it was blue.
   Oh, little bird,
   You never heard
   The song I sang to you.

Myra Cohn Livingston

Sally and Manda

Sally and Manda are two little lizards
Who gobble up flies in their two little gizzards.
They live by a toadstool near two little hummocks
And crawl all around on their two little stomachs.

Alice B. Campbell

10

Baby Chick

Peck, peck, peck
On the warm brown egg.
Out comes a neck.
Out comes a leg.

How does a chick
Who's not been about,
Discover the trick
Of how to get out?

Aileen Fisher

The Little Turtle

There was a little turtle.
He lived in a box.
He swam in a puddle.
He climbed on the rocks.

He snapped at a mosquito.
He snapped at a flea.
He snapped at a minnow.
And he snapped at me.

He caught the mosquito.
He caught the flea.
He caught the minnow.
But he didn't catch me.

Vachel Lindsay

Fishing

John went fishing,
He caught the biggest fish,
Huge enough and good enough
To fill a supper dish.

Tom went fishing,
He caught a little newt,
A stringy weed,
A tadpole,
And one old boot.

Ivy O. Eastwick

13

Sizes

DEAR little pig,
CUTE little pig,
You are born so teeny,
And you grow so BIG!

Eleanor Graham Vance

14

Mr. Rabbit

Mr. Rabbit has a habit
That is very cute to see.

He wrinkles up and crinkles up
His little nose at me.

I like my little rabbit,
And I like his little brother,

And we have a lot of fun
Making faces at each other!

Dixie Willson

Our Pussy Cat

There's a place on the book shelf, way up high,
Where our pussy cat specially likes to lie.
She jumps to the shelf from the back of a chair
And looks down on us from away up there.
Her tail hangs down with never a bend
But a come-and-go kink at the very end.
All day she lies up there on the shelf—
But at night she goes out in the dark by herself!

Alice White North

Pet

I wish I had a tiger cub
   To pat, pat, pat.
He'd be tiny for a tiger
   But ENORMOUS for a cat.

Eleanor Graham Vance

17

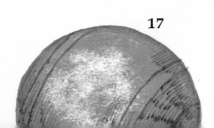

I Like Dogs

I like dogs—
Big dogs,
Little dogs,
Fat dogs,
Doggy dogs,
Old dogs,
Puppy dogs.

I like dogs—
A dog that is barking
over the hill,
A dog that is dreaming
very still,
A dog that is running
wherever he will.
I like dogs.

Margaret Wise Brown

19

Mr. Goat Explains

A boot or a bonnet (if either be handy)
I eagerly nibble as though it were candy;
The stump of a cabbage I eagerly nibble;
A goat doesn't quibble.

Al Graham

20

Foal

Come trotting up
Beside your mother,
Little skinny.

Lay your neck across
Her back, and whinny,
Little foal.
You think you're a horse
Because you can trot—
But you're not.

Your eyes are so wild,
And each leg is as tall
As a pole;

And you're only a skittish
Child, after all,
Little foal.

Mary Britton Miller

21

The Neck

The neck
Of a calf
Is a half
Of a half
Of a half
Of a half
Of a half
Of a half
Of a half
Of a half
    Of the size
    Of the neck
    Of a little
    Giraffe.

        Ilo Orleans

22

If You Should Meet a Crocodile

If you should meet a crocodile,
    Don't take a stick and poke him;
Ignore the welcome in his smile,
    Be careful not to stroke him.
For as he sleeps upon the Nile,
    He thinner gets and thinner;
And whene'er you meet a crocodile
    He's ready for his dinner.

Author Unknown

23

Why Nobody Pets the Lion at the Zoo

The morning that the world began
The Lion growled a growl at Man.

And I suspect the Lion might
(If he'd been closer) have tried a bite.

I think that's as it ought to be
And not as it was taught to me.

I think the Lion has a right
To growl a growl and bite a bite.

But if you look him in the eye
You'll find the Lion's rather shy.

He really wants someone to pet him.
The trouble is: his teeth won't let him.

He has a heart of gold beneath
But the Lion just can't trust his teeth.

John Ciardi

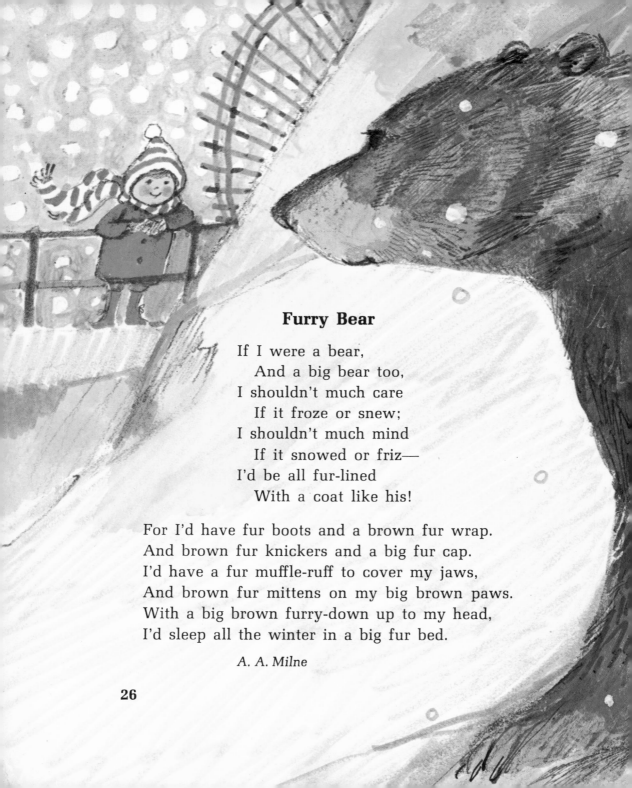

Furry Bear

If I were a bear,
    And a big bear too,
I shouldn't much care
    If it froze or snew;
I shouldn't much mind
    If it snowed or friz—
I'd be all fur-lined
    With a coat like his!

For I'd have fur boots and a brown fur wrap.
And brown fur knickers and a big fur cap.
I'd have a fur muffle-ruff to cover my jaws,
And brown fur mittens on my big brown paws.
With a big brown furry-down up to my head,
I'd sleep all the winter in a big fur bed.

     A. A. Milne

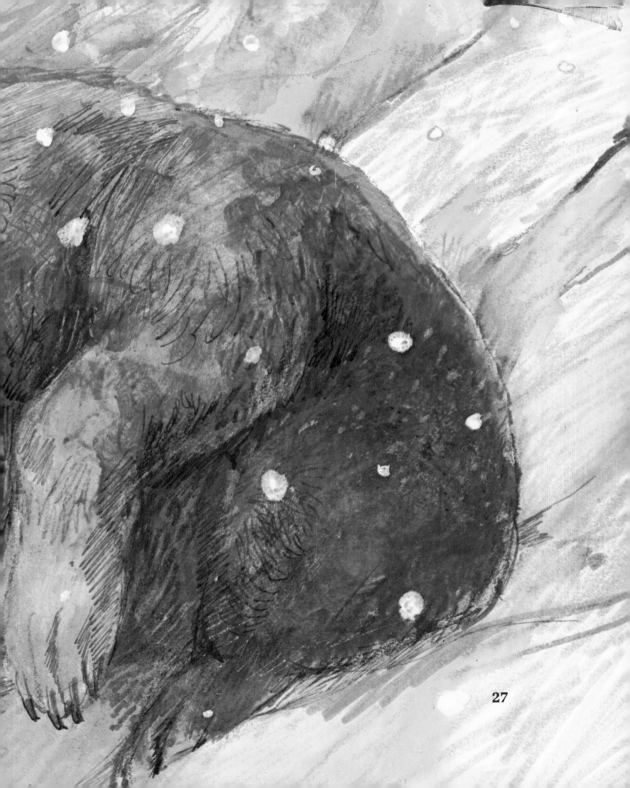

27

Bigger

This cow is big. Her eyes are round.
She makes a very scary sound.

I'm rather glad the fence is tall—
I don't feel quite so weak and small.

And yet I'm not afraid. You see,
I'm six years old—and she's just three.

Dorothy Brown Thompson

Camel

The camel's a mammal
who grouches and grumps.
I think that he wishes
he didn't have humps.

Maxine W. Kumin

29

Rhinoceros

The rhino, in loose-fitting hide,
Is overweight and under-eyed.
The tooth it wears upon its face
Appears to me quite out of place.
But, being used to thus and such,
The rhino doesn't care too much
And looks upon its rhino baby
As something rather pretty—maybe.

Julia Hurd Strong

30

Holding Hands

Elephants walking
Along the trails

Are holding hands
By holding tails.

Trunks and tails
Are handy things

When elephants walk
In Circus rings.

Elephants work
And elephants play

And elephants walk
And feel so gay.

And when they walk—
It never fails

They're holding hands
By holding tails.

Lenore M. Link

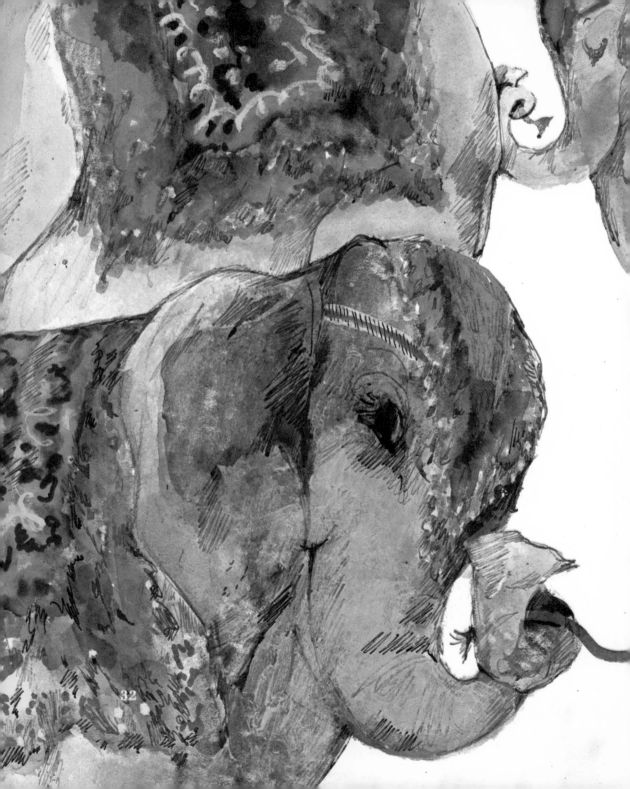

32